BEATRICE
NEW CLOTHES

Written by Pam Halter

Illustrated by Kim Sponaugle

"See how the lilies of the field grow.
They do not labor or spin.
Yet I tell you that not even Solomon in all his
splendor was dressed like one of these."

Matthew 6:28–29

4

Beatrice threw herself on her bed and burst into tears.
Sobbing loudly, she hugged her dolly
and cried into her pillow.

Mommy came in and sat down on the bed. "What's wrong, dear?" she asked.

Beatrice sat up and wiped her eyes. "Oh, Mommy! Everyone laughed at me today!" she cried.

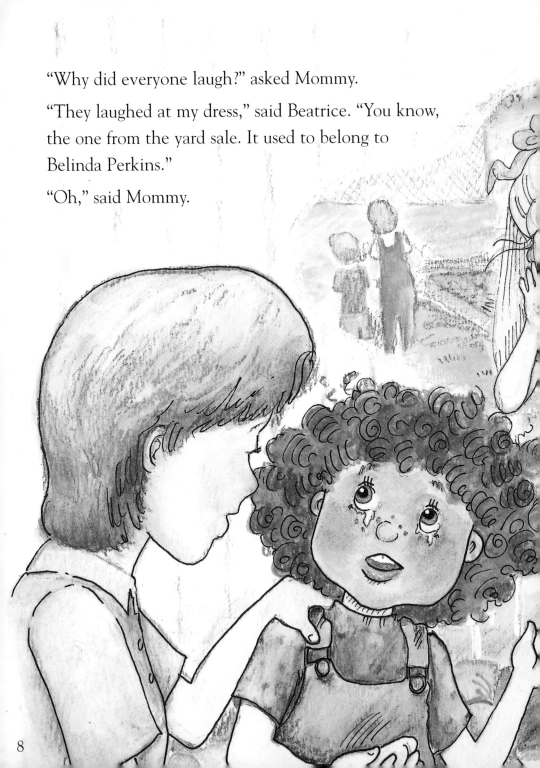

"Why did everyone laugh?" asked Mommy.

"They laughed at my dress," said Beatrice. "You know, the one from the yard sale. It used to belong to Belinda Perkins."

"Oh," said Mommy.

"Belinda Perkins is in third grade," continued Beatrice. "Her daddy is a lawyer and they're rich!"

"Belinda doesn't have to wear hand-me-downs or clothes from yard sales."

"Oh," said Mommy, again.

"It's not fair!" Beatrice burst out. "Why do I have to wear hand-me-downs and yard-sale clothes? Why can't I have new clothes like Belinda Perkins?"

Mommy smiled. "Well, dear, your daddy doesn't have a job that pays enough money for new clothes all the time," she said gently. "There is nothing wrong with second-hand clothes."

"But everyone laughs when I wear someone else's clothes!" sobbed
Beatrice.

Mommy hugged her close. "Oh, Beatrice, don't you see that Jesus provides us with all we need? If there were no yard sales or hand-me-downs, you might have only one or two outfits to wear instead of lots!"

"But it hurts when they laugh at me," said Beatrice.

"I know, dear," said Mommy. "I'll try to think of something."

On Saturday morning, Beatrice was playing with Dolly when Mommy came into the room. "Beatrice, I have an idea," she said. "Why don't we take some of your old clothes and make them into new ones?"

"How can we do that?" asked Beatrice.

"Come with me," said Mommy.

Beatrice and her mom went into the room where Mommy worked at home, sewing and repairing clothes for other people. "There are lots of things here that we can use to dress up your old clothes," said Mommy. "And that way, we will make new clothes out of your old ones!"

Beatrice smiled.

All day Beatrice and Mommy worked on her old clothes. By supper time Beatrice looked at her new wardrobe. "Belinda Perkins can't make fun of these now!" she thought happily.

Beatrice held up a dress. It was the one from Belinda's yard sale, but you never would have guessed. It looked so different now!

Beatrice imagined the look on Belinda's face when she wore her "new" dress to school next week. She hugged the dress to herself and giggled.

"Thank you, Mommy!" she exclaimed. Mommy smiled.
"You're welcome, dear."

When she wore her new outfit to dinner, Daddy said she looked beautiful. And even Bradley said, "Cool!"

That night, Beatrice said a special thank-You prayer to God for sending Jesus, AND for providing her with lots of new clothes.

"Maybe Mommy can make new clothes for Dolly," she thought as she drifted off to sleep. "And a new collar for Ross …"

Ross thumped his tail and rolled over.

Dolly snuggled in Beatrice's arms. And the new clothes hung proudly in the closet.

Hi kids!

Do you know that God gives us everything we need? He gives us the things we need, and sometimes even the things we want.

Do you know the very best thing God gave to us? He gave Jesus to us as our Savior. Because Jesus died on the cross and rose again, we are made new. Jesus forgives our sins and He will help us love others with a brand new heart full of His love.